Legends: Water Monsters and Unicorns

Story by Diane DeFord

Illustrations by Ross Watton

Dominie Press, Inc.

Nessie, the Loch Ness Monster

In the land of the mist in Scotland there is a quiet, deep lake. At least, Loch Ness is usually quiet. But early one morning, Mr. and Mrs. Spicer were driving on the new road next to the lake.

The year was 1933. They saw an unusual animal crossing the road. First its long neck appeared in the lights of the car. Then the Spicers saw its huge, ponderous body. It was thirty to forty feet tall. In seconds, the beast crossed the road. It lurched toward the Loch and disappeared into its depths.

This was not the first sighting of the mysterious creature in Loch Ness. But it was the first sighting of it on land.

In January of the next year, a motorcyclist named Mr. Grant almost collided with the monster. He was going home at about one o'clock in the morning. He jumped off his motorcycle to follow the creature. It headed toward the lake. The moon was bright, so Mr. Grant could see the small head on the monster's very large body. By the time he reached the lake, he saw only the ripples on the water.

There have been sightings of Nessie, the Loch Ness monster, since the 6th century. But the reports from the past 100 years have created the most interest.

The people who live near Loch Ness are the best sources of information. A young girl working as a maid in a home near the lake described the animal. It had a neck like a giraffe, skin like an elephant, and short flippers for front legs. She said it was one of the biggest animals she had ever seen.

In recent years, film crews and photographers have tried to capture images of Nessie. Most of the pictures show a large creature in the water, but no one can be sure of what it is.

There have even been people using sonar equipment to try to take underwater pictures of the creature. But to date, no one has been able to verify that the Loch Ness monster exists. However, each day another name is added to the long list of people who say they have seen this amazing creature.

Stop here. Read the rest of the book silently.

The Unicorn

A long time ago, unicorns were fairly common creatures. A story is told about why we no longer have unicorns in the world. Noah collected two of every animal for his ark. The unicorns were waiting to be loaded. As the water rose higher and higher, the unicorns played in the water. They didn't want to get in the boat. And so they were left behind. That could explain why no one sees unicorns in today's world.

In 1960, an American professor was doing research in Spain. He discovered a letter from a man who claimed to have seen a unicorn on an expedition to the New World with Hernan Cortes, the famous Spanish explorer.

In 1961, another man, Robert Vavra, bought a journal in a flea market in Spain. It was dated 1836 and was written by Rudolf Springer. The journal contained a study of unicorns, complete with drawings of the animals Mr. Springer observed in Africa.

In several conversations years later, Mr. Vavra heard of other people who said they saw unicorns. He was so interested in seeing unicorns that he put together an expedition in 1981. Mr. Vavra and his team went to the foot of Mount Kilimanjaro, the highest peak in Africa.

In his journal, Mr. Springer wrote the directions for making a special body oil. He claimed that the oil would enable a person to get close to elephants, lions, and unicorns. Mr. Vavra made this oil to take on his expedition.

The directions were carefully worded. In order to get close to a unicorn, Mr. Vavra had to follow the steps outlined in the journal. The directions also explained how to talk to unicorns and the type of sounds to make.

Mr. Vavra was on safari in Kenya for two weeks before he got close to his first wild animal, an elephant. He wanted to test the special body oil, so he had two men stay at the car while he walked up to the elephant.

The journal described what might happen. It said the elephant might charge, but it would be a mock charge. So Robert Vavra stood his ground as the huge elephant charged. The dust swirled around as the elephant stopped right beside him. Then the elephant's trunk touched his shoulder. It sniffed the air and

smelled him. Its white tusks touched his leg. He shouted at his men, "Take some pictures!" His voice made the elephant turn away and disappear into the trees.

Unfortunately, the men were so scared by the elephant that they didn't take any pictures. But one of them did draw a picture.

After the encounter with the elephant, Mr. Vavra wanted to find a unicorn more than ever. He continued his expedition in Kenya.

The story of how he was able to get close enough to have a unicorn touch him and to get photographs of this wondrous creature is well worth reading.

He describes how the unicorn pulled leaves from trees and how it snorted, sighed, and shook its head and mane. It is possible to imagine what it is like to be so close to an amazing animal.

Robert Vavra is a photographer and naturalist. His story was published in *Life* magazine and in a book he titled *Unicorns I Have Known*. The photographs he took are beautiful. They prove that the white, one-horned unicorn does exist.

Publisher: Raymond Yuen
Consultant: Adria F. Klein
Editor: Bob Rowland
Designer: Natalie Chupil
Illustrator: Ross Watton

Published by:

🔁 Dominie Press, Inc.

1949 Kellogg Avenue
Carlsbad, California 92008 USA

www.dominie.com

ISBN 0-7685-0654-9

Printed in Singapore by PH Productions Pte Ltd

2 3 4 5 6 PH 02 01

ITP